'An ass, clothed
in the skin of
a lion . . .'

AESOP

Generally believed to have lived in the 6th century BC.

AESOP IN PENGUIN CLASSICS
The Complete Fables

AESOP

The Dolphins, the Whales and the Gudgeon

Translated by
Robert *and* Olivia Temple

PENGUIN BOOKS

PENGUIN CLASSICS

Published by the Penguin Group
Penguin Books Ltd, 80 Strand, London WC2R ORL, England
Penguin Group (USA) Inc., 375 Hudson Street, New York, New York 10014, USA
Penguin Group (Canada), 90 Eglinton Avenue East, Suite 700, Toronto, Ontario,
Canada M4P 2Y3 (a division of Pearson Penguin Canada Inc.)
Penguin Ireland, 25 St Stephen's Green, Dublin 2, Ireland
(a division of Penguin Books Ltd)
Penguin Group (Australia), 707 Collins Street, Melbourne, Victoria 3008, Australia
(a division of Pearson Australia Group Pty Ltd)
Penguin Books India Pvt Ltd, 11 Community Centre, Panchsheel Park,
New Delhi – 110 017, India
Penguin Group (NZ), 67 Apollo Drive, Rosedale, Auckland 0632, New Zealand
(a division of Pearson New Zealand Ltd)
Penguin Books (South Africa) (Pty) Ltd, Block D, Rosebank Office Park,
181 Jan Smuts Avenue, Parktown North, Gauteng 2193, South Africa

Penguin Books Ltd, Registered Offices: 80 Strand, London WC2R ORL, England

www.penguin.com

This selection published in Penguin Classics 2015
001

Translation copyright © Robert and Olivia Temple, 1998

Set in 9/11.9 pt Baskerville 10 Pro
Typeset by Jouve (UK), Milton Keynes
Printed in Great Britain by Clays Ltd, St Ives plc

A CIP catalogue record for this book is available from the British Library

ISBN: 978-0-141-39843-3

www.greenpenguin.co.uk

The Eagle, the Jackdaw and the Shepherd

An eagle, dropping suddenly from a high rock, carried off a lamb. A jackdaw saw this, was smitten by a sense of rivalry and determined to do the same. So, with a great deal of noise, he pounced upon a ram. But his claws merely got caught in the thick ringlets of the ram's fleece, and no matter how frantically he flapped his wings, he was unable to get free and take flight.

Finally the shepherd bestirred himself, hurried up to the jackdaw and got hold of him. He clipped the end of his wings and, when evening fell, he carried him back for his children. The children wanted to know what sort of bird this was. So the shepherd replied:

'As far as I can see, it's a jackdaw, but it would like us to think it's an eagle!'

Just so, to compete with the powerful is not only not worth the effort and labour lost, but also brings mockery and calamity upon us.

The Cat and the Cock

A cat who had caught a cock wanted to give a plausible reason for devouring it. So she accused it of annoying people by crowing at night and disturbing their sleep.

The cock defended himself by saying that he did it to be helpful. For, if he woke people up, it was to summon them to their accustomed work.

Then the cat produced another grievance and accused the cock of insulting Nature by his relationship with his mother and sisters.

The cock replied that in this also he was serving his master's interests, since it was thanks to this that the chickens laid lots of eggs.

'Ah well!' cried the cat, 'I'm not going to go without food just because you can produce a lot of justifications!' And she ate the cock.

This fable shows that someone with a wicked nature who is determined to do wrong, when he cannot do so in the guise of a good man, does his evil deeds openly.

The Goat and the Donkey

A man kept a goat and a donkey. The goat became jealous of the donkey, because it was so well fed. So she said to him:

'What with turning the millstone and all the burdens you carry, your life is just a torment without end.'

She advised him to pretend to have epilepsy and to fall into a hole in order to get some rest. The donkey followed her advice, fell down and was badly bruised all over. His master went to get the vet and asked him for a remedy for these injuries. The vet prescribed an infusion of goat's lung; this remedy would surely restore him to health. As a result, the man sacrificed the goat to cure the donkey.

Whosoever schemes against others owes his own misfortune to himself.

The Two Cocks and the Eagle

Two cockerels were fighting over some hens. One triumphed and saw the other off. The defeated one then withdrew into a thicket where he hid himself. The victor fluttered up into the air and sat atop a high wall, where he began to crow with a loud voice.

Straight away an eagle fell upon him and carried him off. And, from then on, the cockerel hidden in the shadows possessed all the hens at his leisure.

This fable shows that the Lord resisteth the proud but giveth grace unto the humble.

The Fisherman and
the Large and Small Fish

A fisherman drew in his net from the sea. He could catch big fish, which he spread out in the sun, but the small fish slipped through the mesh, escaping into the sea.

People of a mediocre fortune escape danger easily, but one rarely sees a man of great note escape when there is a disaster.

The Fox and the Woodcutter

A fox who was fleeing ahead of some hunters saw a wood-cutter and pleaded with him to find a hiding-place. The woodcutter promised to hide him in his hut, and did so. Some moments later the huntsmen arrived and asked the woodcutter if he had seen a fox in the vicinity. He replied in words that he had not seen one go past, but by signalling with his hands he indicated where the fox was hidden. The huntsmen, however, took no notice of his gestures and simply took him at his word.

After they had gone, the fox emerged from the hut without saying anything. When the woodcutter reproached him for showing no gratitude for having saved him, the fox replied:

'I would thank you if your gestures and your conduct had agreed with your words.'

One could apply this fable to men who make protestations of virtue but who actually behave like rascals.

The Fox and the Billy-goat

A fox, having fallen into a well, was faced with the prospect of being stuck there. But then a billy-goat came along to that same well because he was thirsty and saw the fox. He asked him if the water was good.

The fox decided to put a brave face on it and gave a tremendous speech about how wonderful the water was down there, so very excellent. So the billy-goat climbed down the well, thinking only of his thirst. When he had had a good drink, he asked the fox what he thought was the best way to get back up again.

The fox said:

'Well, I have a very good way to do that. Of course, it will mean our working together. If you just push your front feet up against the wall and hold your horns up in the air as high as you can, I will climb up on to them, get out, and then I can pull you up behind me.'

The billy-goat willingly consented to this idea, and the fox briskly clambered up the legs, the shoulders, and finally the horns of his companion. He found himself at the mouth of the well, pulled himself out, and immediately scampered off. The billy-goat shouted after him, reproaching him for breaking their agreement of mutual assistance. The fox came back to the top of the well and shouted down to the billy-goat:

'Ha! If you had as many brains as you have hairs on your

chin, you wouldn't have got down there in the first place without thinking of how you were going to get out again.'

It is thus that sensible men should not undertake any action without having first examined the end result.

The Man Bitten by an Ant, and Hermes

One day, a sailing ship sank to the bottom of the sea with all its passengers. A man who was a witness of the shipwreck claimed that the decrees of the gods were unjust, for to lose a single impious person they had also made the innocent perish.

There were a great many ants on the spot where he was standing. As he was saying this, it happened that one of them bit him. In order to kill it, he crushed them all.

Then Hermes appeared to him, and struck him with his wand [*rhabdos*], saying:

'And now do you not admit that the gods judge men in the same way you judge the ants?'

Don't blaspheme against the gods. When misfortune befalls you, examine your own faults.

The Cheat

A poor man, being very ill and getting worse, promised the gods to sacrifice to them one hundred oxen if they saved him from death. The gods, wishing to put him to the test, restored him to health very quickly. Soon he was up and out of bed.

But, as he didn't really have any oxen, he modelled one hundred of them out of tallow and burned them on an altar, saying:

'Receive my votive offering, oh gods!'

But the gods, wanting to trick him in their turn, sent him a dream saying that if he would go to the seashore it would result in one thousand Athenian drachmas for him. Unable to contain his joy, he ran to the beach, where he came across some pirates who took him away and sold him into slavery. And they did indeed obtain one thousand Athenian drachmas for him.

This fable is well applied to a liar.

The Man and the Lion Travelling Together

A man and a lion were travelling along together one day when they began to argue about which of them was the stronger. Just then they passed a stone statue representing a man strangling a lion.

'There, you see, we are stronger than you,' said the man, pointing it out to the lion.

But the lion smiled and replied:

'If lions could make statues, you would see plenty of men under the paws of lions.'

Many people boast of how brave and fearless they are, but when put to the test are exposed as frauds.

The Bear and the Fox

A bear once boasted to a fox that he had a great love for mankind, since he made it a point never to eat a corpse.

The fox replied:

'I wish to heaven you would mangle the dead rather than the living!'

This fable unmasks the covetous who live in hypocrisy and vainglory.

The Frogs Who Demanded a King

The frogs, annoyed with the anarchy in which they lived, sent a deputation to Zeus to ask him to give them a king. Zeus, seeing that they were but very simple creatures, threw a piece of wood into their marsh. The frogs were so alarmed by the sudden noise that they plunged into the depths of the bog. But when the piece of wood did not move, they clambered out again. They developed such a contempt for this new king that they jumped on his back and crouched there.

The frogs were deeply ashamed at having such a king, so they sent a second deputation to Zeus asking him to change their monarch. For the first was too passive and did nothing.

Zeus now became impatient with them and sent down a water-serpent [*hydra*] which seized them and ate them all up.

This fable teaches us that it is better to be ruled by passive, worthless men who bear no spitefulness than by productive but wicked ones.

The Ox-driver and Herakles

An ox-driver was bringing a wagon towards a town. The wagon fell down into a deep ravine. But instead of doing anything to get it out, the ox-driver stood without doing a thing, and merely invoked Herakles among all the gods whom he particularly honoured. Herakles appeared to him and said:

'Put your hand to the wheels, goad the oxen, and do not invoke the gods without making some effort yourself. Otherwise you will invoke them in vain.'

The House-ferret and Aphrodite

A house-ferret, having fallen in love with a handsome young man, begged Aphrodite, goddess of love, to change her into a human girl. The goddess took pity on this passion and changed her into a gracious young girl. The young man, when he saw her, fell in love with her and led her to his home. As they rested in the nuptial chamber [*thalamos*], Aphrodite, wanting to see if in changing body the house-ferret had also changed in character, released a mouse in the middle of the room. The house-ferret, forgetting her present condition, leapt up from the bed and chased the mouse in order to eat it. Then the indignant goddess changed her back to her former state.

Bad people who change their appearance do not change their character.

The House-ferret and the File

A house-ferret slipped into a blacksmith's workshop and began to lick the file that she found there. Now it happened that using her tongue thus, the blood flowed from it. But she was delighted, imagining that she had extracted something from the iron. And in the end she lost her tongue.

This fable is aimed at people who pick arguments with others, thereby doing harm to themselves.

The Ploughman and the Frozen Snake

One winter, a ploughman found a snake stiff with cold. He took pity on it, picked it up and put it under his shirt. When the snake had warmed up again against the man's chest, it reverted to its nature, struck out and killed its benefactor. When he realized that he was dying, the man bemoaned:

'I well deserve it, for taking pity on a wicked wretch.'

This fable shows that perversity of nature does not change under the influence of kindness.

The Wife and Her Drunken Husband

There was a woman whose husband was a drunkard. To get the better of him and his vice she devised a plan. She waited for the moment when her husband was so drunk that he was like a corpse, then she heaved him up over her shoulders, carried him to the cemetery and dumped him there. When she thought he had slept it off, she went back to the cemetery and knocked on the door of the vault.

'Who's that at the door?' the drunkard called out.

'It's me, who comes to bring food for the dead,' replied his wife mournfully.

'Don't bring me anything to eat, my good man. Bring me more to drink. You distress me by talking about food and not drink.'

The wife, beating her breast, cried out:

'Alas! How miserable I am! My plan has had no effect on you, husband! For not only are you not sober but you have become even worse. Your weakness has now become second nature to you.'

This fable shows that you shouldn't become habituated to a loose way of life, for there comes a time when habit forces itself upon you, whether you like it or not.

The Woman and the Hen

A widow had a hen which laid an egg every day. She imagined that if she gave the hen more barley it would lay twice a day. So she increased the hen's ration accordingly. But the hen became fat and wasn't even capable of laying one egg a day.

This fable shows that if, through greed, you look for more than you have, you lose even that which you do possess.

The Dolphins, the Whales and the Gudgeon

Some dolphins and some whales were engaged in battle. As the fight went on and became desperate, a gudgeon poked his head above the surface of the water and tried to reconcile them. But one of the dolphins retorted:

'It is less humiliating for us to fight to the death between ourselves than to have you for a mediator.'

Similarly, certain nobodies think they are somebody when they interfere in a public row.

The Stag at the Spring and the Lion

A stag, oppressed by thirst, came to a spring to drink. After having a drink, he saw the shadowy figure of himself in the water. He much admired his fine antlers, their grandeur and extent. But he was discontented with his legs, which he thought looked thin and feeble. He remained there deep in reverie when suddenly a lion sprang out at him and chased him. The stag fled rapidly and ran a great distance, for the stag's advantage is his legs, whereas a lion's is his heart. As long as they were in open ground, the stag easily outdistanced the lion. But they entered a wooded area and the stag's antlers became entangled in the branches, bringing him to a halt so that he was caught by the lion.

As he was on the point of death, the stag said:

'How unfortunate I am! My feet, which I had denigrated, could have saved me, whereas my antlers, on which I prided myself, have caused my death!'

And thus, in dangerous situations it is often the friends whom we suspect who save us, while those on whom we rely betray us.

The Kid on the Roof of the House, and the Wolf

A kid who had wandered on to the roof of a house saw a wolf pass by and he began to insult and jeer at it. The wolf replied:

'Hey, you there! It's not you who mock me but the place on which you are standing.'

This fable shows that often it is the place and the occasion which give one the daring to defy the powerful.

The Two Enemies

Two men who loathed each other were sailing in the same boat. One took up his position at the stern and the other at the prow. A storm blew up and the boat was on the point of sinking. The man at the stern asked the helmsman which part of the vessel would go down first. 'The prow,' he said. 'Then,' replied the man, 'death will no longer be sad for me, if I can see my enemy die first.'

This fable shows that many people are not in the least disturbed at the harm that befalls them, provided they can see their enemies' downfall first.

The Sun and the Frogs

It was summer, and people were celebrating the wedding feast of the Sun. All the animals were rejoicing at the event, and only the frogs were left to join in the gaiety. But a protesting frog called out:

'Fools! How can you rejoice? The Sun dries out all the marshland. If he takes a wife and has a child similar to himself, imagine how much more we would suffer!'

Plenty of empty-headed people are jubilant about things which they have no cause to celebrate.

The Mule

A mule who had grown fat on barley began to get frisky, saying to herself: 'My father is a fast-running horse, and I take after him in every way.' But, one day, she was forced to run a race. At the end of the race she looked glum and remembered that her father was really an ass.

This fable shows that even if circumstances put a man on show, he ought never to forget his origins, for life is full of uncertainty.

The Old Horse

An old horse had been sold to a miller to turn the millstone. When he was harnessed to the mill-wheel he groaned and exclaimed:

'From the turn of the race course I am reduced to such a turn as this!'

Don't be too proud of youthful strength, for many a man's old age is spent in hard work.

The Camel Seen for the First Time

When they first set eyes on a camel, men were afraid. Awed by its huge size, they ran away. But when, in time, they realized its gentleness, they plucked up enough courage to approach it. Then, gradually realizing that it had no temper, they went up to it and grew to hold it in such contempt that they put a bridle on it and gave it to the children to lead.

This fable shows that habit can overcome the fear which awesome things inspire.

The Walnut Tree

A walnut tree which grew on the edge of a path was constantly hit by a volley of stones. It said to itself with a sigh:

'How unlucky I am that year after year I attract insults and suffering.'

This fable is aimed at people who don't withdraw from a source of annoyance for their own good.

The Gardener Watering the Vegetables

A man passed a gardener who was watering his vegetables and he stopped to ask him why the wild vegetables were flourishing and vigorous while the cultivated ones were sickly and puny.

The gardener replied: 'It's because the Earth is a mother to the one and a stepmother to the others.'

Similarly, the children fed by a stepmother are not nourished like those who have their true mother.

The Kithara-player

A kithara-player, devoid of talent, sang from morning to night in a house with thickly plastered walls. As the walls echoed with his own sounds he imagined that he had a very beautiful voice. He so overestimated his own voice from then on that he decided to perform in a theatre. But he sang so badly on the stage that he was driven off it by people throwing stones.

Thus, certain orators who, at school, seem to have some talent, reveal their incompetence as soon as they enter the political arena.

The Gnat and the Bull

A gnat had settled on a bull's horn. After he had been there for a while and was about to fly off, he asked the bull whether he would, after all, like him to go away. The bull replied:

'When you came, I didn't feel you. And when you go I won't feel you either.'

One could apply this fable to the feeble person whose presence or absence is neither helpful nor harmful.

The Ageing Lion and the Fox

A lion who was getting old and could no longer obtain his food by force decided that he must resort to trickery instead. So he retired to a cave and lay down pretending to be ill. Thus, whenever any animals came to his cave to visit him, he ate them all as they appeared.

When many animals had disappeared, a fox figured out what was happening. He went to see the lion but stood at a safe distance outside the cave and asked him how he was.

'Oh, not very well,' said the lion. 'But why don't you come in?'

But the fox said:

'I would come inside if I hadn't seen that a lot of footprints are pointing inwards towards your cave but none are pointing out.'

Wise men note the indications of dangers and thus avoid them.

The Snake, the House-ferret and the Mice

A snake and a house-ferret were fighting each other in a certain house where they lived. The mice of the house, who were forever being eaten by one or the other of them, came quietly out of their holes when they heard them fighting. At the sight of the mice, the two combatants gave up their battle and turned on the mice.

It is the same in the city-states [poleōn]; *people who interfere in the quarrels of the demagogues become, without suspecting it, the victims of both sides.*

The Snake and the Crab

A snake and a crab frequented the same place. The crab continually behaved towards the snake in all simplicity and kindness. But the snake was always cunning and perverse. The crab ceaselessly urged the snake to behave towards him with honesty and to imitate his own manner towards him; he did not listen. So, indignant, the crab waited for an occasion when the snake was asleep, grabbed it and killed it. Seeing it stretched out dead, the crab called out:

'Hey, friend! It's no use being straight now that you are dead, you should have done that when I was urging you to before; then you wouldn't have had to be put to death!'

One could rightly tell this fable with regard to people who, during their life, are wicked towards their friends and do them a service after their death.

The Trodden-on Snake and Zeus

The snake, heavily trodden on so often by men's feet, went to Zeus to complain. Zeus said to it:

'If you had bitten the first one who trod on you, the second one would not have tried to do so.'

This fable shows that those who hold their own against the first people who attack them make themselves formidable to others who do so.

The Child Catching Locusts, and the Scorpion

A child was catching locusts in front of the city wall. After having caught a certain number of them, he saw a scorpion. He took it for a locust and, cupping his hand, was about to put it in his palm when the scorpion, rearing his spike, said to the child:

'Would that you had done that! For then you would have lost the locusts that you have already caught!'

This fable shows us that we should not behave in the same way towards good and wicked people.

The Child and the Raven

A woman consulted the diviners about her infant son. They predicted that he would be killed by a raven [*korax*]. Terror-stricken by this prediction, she had a huge chest constructed and shut the boy up inside it to prevent him from being killed by a raven. And every day, at a given time, she opened it and gave the child as much food as he needed. Then, one day when she had opened the chest and was putting back the lid, the child foolishly stuck his head out. So it happened that the *korax* [hooked handle] on the chest fell down on to the top of his head and killed him.

The Flea and the Man

Once, a flea was irritating a man relentlessly. So he caught it and said to it:

'Who are you, who makes a meal of all my limbs, biting me all over at random?'

The flea answered:

'That's the way we live. Don't kill me, for I can't do much harm.'

The man started to laugh and said:

'You're going to die now, and at my hands, for however great or small the harm it is imperative to stop you breeding.'

This fable shows that it is not necessary to take pity on the wicked, however strong or feeble he may be.

The Jackdaw and the Ravens

A jackdaw who grew larger in size than the other jackdaws disdained their company. So he took himself off to the ravens and asked if he could share his life with them. But the ravens, unfamiliar with his shape and his voice, mobbed him and chased him away. So, rejected by them, he went back to be with the jackdaws. But the jackdaws, outraged at his defection, refused to have him back. And thus he was an outcast from the society of both jackdaws and ravens.

It is similar with people. Those who abandon their own country in preference for another are in low esteem there for being foreigners, but despised by their compatriots because they have scorned them.

The Man Bitten by a Dog

A man who had been bitten by a dog roamed far and wide, looking for someone to heal his wound. Someone told him all he had to do was wipe the blood from his wound with some bread and throw the bread to the dog which had bitten him. To this the injured man replied:

'But if I did that, every dog in the city would bite me.'

Similarly, if you indulge someone's wickedness, you provoke him to do even more harm.

The Sleeping Dog and the Wolf

A dog lay asleep in front of a farm building. A wolf pounced on him and was going to make a meal of him, when the dog begged him not to eat him straight away:

'At the moment,' he said, 'I am thin and lean. But wait a little while; my masters will be celebrating a wedding feast. I will get some good mouthfuls and will fatten up and will be a much better meal for you.'

The wolf believed him and went on his way. A little while later he came back and found the dog asleep on top of the house. He stopped below and shouted up to him, reminding him of their agreement. Then the dog said:

'Oh, wolf! If you ever see me asleep in front of the farm again, don't wait for the wedding banquet!'

This fable shows that wise people, when they get out of a fix, take care of themselves all the rest of their life.

The Dog with a Bell

A dog furtively bit people, so his master hung a bell on him to warn everyone he was coming. Then the dog, shaking his bell, swaggered about in the agora. An old bitch said to him:

'What have you got to strut about? You don't wear the bell as a result of any virtue, but to advertise your secret ill nature.'

The secret spitefulness of boastful people is exposed by their vainglorious behaviour.

The Wolf and the Lamb

A wolf saw a lamb drinking at a stream and wanted to devise a suitable pretext for devouring it. So, although he was himself upstream, he accused the lamb of muddying the water and preventing him from drinking. The lamb replied that he only drank with the tip of his tongue and that, besides, being downstream he couldn't muddy the water upstream. The wolf's stratagem having collapsed, he replied:

'But last year you insulted my father.'

'I wasn't even born then,' replied the lamb.

So the wolf resumed:

'Whatever you say to justify yourself, I will eat you all the same.'

This fable shows that when some people decide upon doing harm, the fairest defence has no effect whatever.

The Wolf and the Young Lamb
Taking Refuge in a Temple

A wolf pursued a young lamb, who took refuge in a temple. The wolf called out to it and said that the sacrificer would offer it up to the god if he found the lamb there. But the lamb replied:

'Ah well! I would prefer to be a victim of a god than to die by your hand.'

This fable shows that if one is being driven towards death, it is better to die with honour.

The Diviner

A diviner was sitting plying his trade in the agora. Suddenly, someone rushed up to him and said that the front door of his house was wide open and the contents gone. The diviner leapt up in consternation and ran home, gasping to see what had happened. A passer-by who saw him running called out:

'Hey there! You who pride yourself on foretelling the future for others! Can't you foresee what will happen to yourself?'

One could apply this fable to people who order their own lives woefully but who dabble in controlling affairs which are not their concern.

The Field Mouse and the Town Mouse

A field mouse had a town mouse for a friend. The field mouse invited the town mouse to dinner in the country. When he saw that there was only barley and corn to eat, the town mouse said:

'Do you know, my friend, that you live like an ant? I, on the other hand, have an abundance of good things. Come home with me and I will share it all with you.'

So they set off together. The house mouse showed his friend some beans and bread-flour, together with some dates, a cheese, honey and fruit. And the field mouse was filled with wonder and blessed him with all his heart, cursing his own lot. Just as they were preparing to start their meal, a man suddenly opened the door. Alarmed by the noise, the mice rushed fearfully into the crevices. Then, as they crept out again to taste some dried figs, someone else came into the room and started looking for something. So they again rushed down the holes to hide. Then the field mouse, forgetting his hunger, sighed, and said to his friend:

'Farewell, my friend. You can eat your fill and be glad of heart, but at the price of a thousand fears and dangers. I, poor little thing, will go on living by nibbling barley and corn without fear or suspicion of anyone.'

*

This fable shows that one should:

> *Live simply and free from passion*
> *Instead of luxuriously in fear and dread.*

The Bat, the Bramble and the Gull

The bat, the bramble and the gull met up with the intention of doing a bit of trading together. The bat went out and borrowed some money to fund the enterprise, the bramble contributed a lot of cloth to be sold and the gull brought a large supply of copper to sell. Then they set sail to go trading, but a violent storm arose which capsized their ship and all the cargo was lost. They were able to save nothing but themselves from the shipwreck.

Ever since that time, the gull has searched the seashore to see if any of his copper might be washed up somewhere, the bat, fearing his creditors, dare not go out by day and only feeds at night, and the bramble clutches the clothes of all those who pass by, hoping to recognize a familiar piece of material.

This fable shows that we always return to those things in which we have a stake.

The Woodcutter and Hermes

A woodcutter who was chopping wood on the banks of a river had lost his axe. Not knowing what to do, he sat himself down on the bank and wept. The god Hermes, learning the cause of his distress, took pity on him. Hermes plunged into the river, brought out a golden axe and asked the woodcutter if this were the one which he had lost. The man said, no, that wasn't the one. So Hermes dived back in again and this time he produced a silver axe. But the woodcutter said, no, that wasn't his axe either.

Hermes plunged in a third time and brought him his own axe. The man said, yes, indeed, this was the very axe which he had lost.

Then Hermes, charmed by his honesty, gave him all three.

Returning to his friends, the woodcutter told them about his adventure. One of them took it into his head to get himself some axes as well. So he set off for the riverbank, threw his axe into the current deliberately and then sat down in tears. Then Hermes appeared to him also and, learning the cause of his tears, he dived in and brought him too a golden axe, asking if it were the one which he had lost.

The man, all joyful, cried out: 'Yes! It is indeed the one!'

But the god, horrified at such effrontery, not only withheld the golden axe but didn't return the man's own.

This fable shows that the gods favour honest people but are hostile to the dishonest.

The Ass Carrying Salt

An ass with a load of salt was crossing a stream. He slipped and fell into the water. Then the salt dissolved, and when he got up his load was lighter than before, so he was delighted. Another time, when he arrived at the bank of a stream with a load of sponges, he thought that if he fell into the water again when he got up the load would be lighter. So he slipped on purpose. But, of course, the sponges swelled up with the water and the ass was unable to get up again, so he drowned and perished.

Thus it is sometimes that people don't suspect that it is their own tricks which land them in disaster.

The Ass, the Cock and the Lion

One day, an ass and a cockerel were feeding together when a lion attacked the ass. The cockerel let out a loud crow and the lion fled, for lions are afraid of the sound of a cock crowing.

The ass, imagining that the lion was fleeing because of him, did not hesitate to rush after him. When he had pursued the lion for about the distance where a cock's crow can no longer be heard, the lion turned round and devoured him. As he was dying, the ass brayed:

'What an unfortunate and stupid fellow I am! Why did I, who was not born to warlike parents, set out to fight?'

This fable shows that the enemy is often portrayed as of no consequence, but when we attack him he destroys us.

The Ass and the Lap-dog
or *The Dog and Its Master*

There was a man who owned a Maltese lap-dog and an ass. He was always playing with the dog. When he dined out, he would bring back titbits and throw them to the dog when it rushed up, wagging its tail. The ass was jealous of this and, one day, trotted up and started frisking around his master. But this resulted in the man getting a kick on the foot, and he grew very angry. So he drove the ass with a stick back to its manger, where he tied it up.

This fable shows that we are not all made to do the same things.

The Ass Who Was Taken for a Lion

An ass, clothed in the skin of a lion, passed himself off in the eyes of everyone as a lion, and made everyone flee from him, both men and animals. But the wind came along and blew off the lion's skin, leaving him naked and exposed. Everyone then fell upon him when they saw this, and beat him with sticks and clubs.

Be poor and ordinary. Don't have pretensions to wealth or you will be exposed to ridicule and danger. For we cannot adapt ourselves to that which is alien to us.

The Bird-catcher and the Wild and Domesticated Pigeons

A bird-catcher spread his nets and tied his domesticated pigeons to them. Then he withdrew and watched from a distance what would happen. Some wild pigeons approached the captive birds and became entangled in the snares. The bird-catcher ran back and started to grab them. As he did so, they reproached the domesticated pigeons because, being of the same race, they should have warned them of the trap. But the domesticated pigeons replied:

'We are more concerned with preventing our master's displeasure than with pleasing our kindred.'

Thus it is with domestic slaves: you can't blame them when, for love of their masters, they fail to show love towards their own kind.

The Hen and the Swallow

A hen found the eggs of a snake and carefully hatched them by sitting upon them and keeping them warm. A swallow, who had seen her doing this, said to her:

'What a fool you are! Why are you rearing these creatures who, once grown, will make you the first victim of their evildoing?'

Perversity cannot be tamed even by the kindest treatment.

The Partridge and the Man

A man caught a partridge while hunting and was about to kill it. She pleaded with him:

'Let me live! In my place I would bring you lots of partridges.'

'All the more reason to kill you,' replied the man, 'since you wish to ensnare your friends and comrades.'

This shows that the man who weaves a plot against his friends will himself fall into danger and ambushes.

The Monkey and the Camel

At an assembly of the beasts, a monkey got up and danced. He was enthusiastically applauded by everyone present. A jealous camel wanted to earn the same praise. He got up and also tried to dance, but he did such absurd things that the other animals became disgusted and beat him out of their sight with sticks.

This fable is suitable for those people who, through envy, compete with those who are their betters.

The Mole and His Mother

A mole – the mole is a blind creature – said to his mother that he could see. To put him to the test, his mother gave him a grain of frankincense [*libanōtos*] and asked him what it was.

'It's a pebble,' he said.

'My child,' replied the mother, 'not only are you bereft of sight, but you have also lost your sense of smell.'

Similarly, boastful people promise the impossible and are proved powerless in the most simple affairs.